P9-CQZ-276

hist whist

e.e. cummings

hist whist

illustrated by Deborah Kogan Ray

A TRUMPET CLUB SPECIAL EDITION

Published by The Trumpet Club
1540 Broadway, New York, New York 10036

Text reprinted from TULIPS & CHIMNEYS by e.e. cummings, edited
by George James Firmage, by permission of Liveright Publishing
Corporation. Copyright 1923, 1925, renewed 1951, 1953, by e.e.
cummings. Copyright © 1973, 1976 by the Trustees for the e.e.
cummings Trust. Copyright © 1973, 1976 by George James Firmage.
Illustrations copyright © 1989 by Deborah Kogan Ray.

All rights reserved. No part of this book may be reproduced or
transmitted in any form or by any means, electronic or mechanical,
including photocopying, recording or by any information storage
and retrieval system, without the written permission of the Pub-
lisher. For information address: Crown Publishers, Inc., 225 Park
Avenue South, New York, New York 10003.

ISBN: 0-440-84458-4

This edition published by arrangement with Crown Publishers, Inc.
Printed in the United States of America
October 1991

10 9 8 7 6 5 4
UPC

hist   whist
little ghostthings
tip-toe
twinkle-toe

little twitchy
witches and tingling
goblins
hob-a-nob   hob-a-nob

little hoppy happy
toad in tweeds
tweeds
little itchy mousies

with scuttling
eyes   rustle and run   and
hidehidehide
whisk

whisk   look out for the old woman
with the wart on her nose
what she'll do to yer
nobody knows

for she knows the devil   ooch
the devil   ouch
the devil
ach   the great

green
dancing
devil
devil

devil
devil

wheeEEE

hist   whist
little ghostthings
tip-toe
twinkle-toe

little twitchy
witches and tingling
goblins
hob-a-nob   hob-a-nob

little hoppy happy
toad in tweeds
tweeds
little itchy mousies

with scuttling
eyes   rustle and run   and
hidehidehide
whisk

whisk   look out for the old woman
with the wart on her nose
what she'll do to yer
nobody knows

for she knows the devil   ooch
the devil   ouch
the devil
ach   the great

green
dancing
devil
devil

devil
devil

        wheeEEE